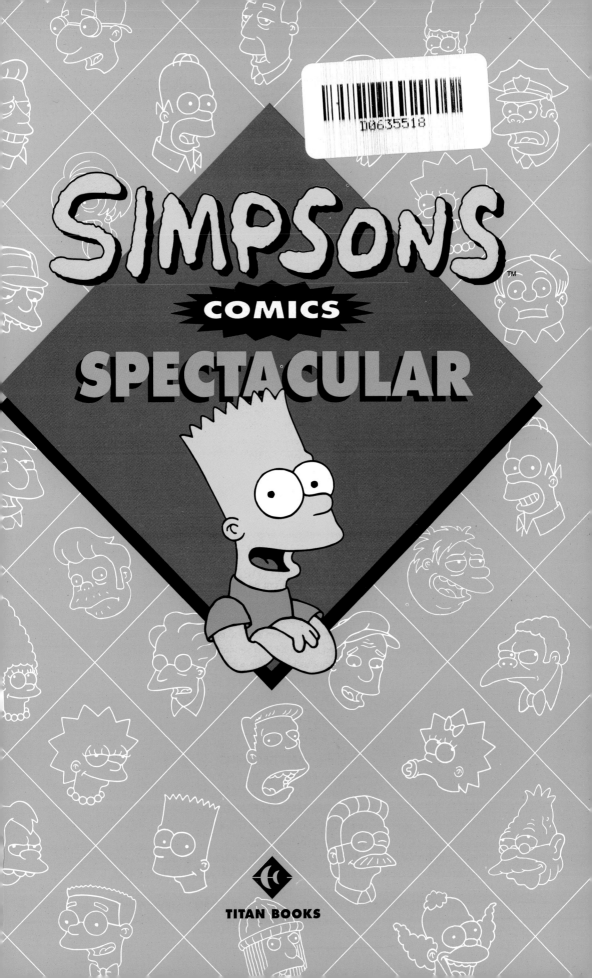

To the loving memory of Snowball I:
You may be gone, but the 30-lb. sack
of kibble you refused to eat remains
(out in the garage next to the paint cans).

SIMPSONS COMICS SPECTACULAR Copyright ©1995 by
Bongo Entertainment, Inc. All rights reserved. Printed in Canada.
No part of this book may be used or reproduced in any
manner whatsoever without written permission except in the
case of brief quotations embodied in critical articles and reviews.
For information address Bongo Comics Group c/o Titan Books.

Published in the UK by Titan Publishing Group Ltd., 144 Southwark Street,
London SE1 0UP, under licence from Bongo Entertainment, Inc.

This book is sold subject to the condition that it shall not, by way of trade
or otherwise, be lent, resold, hired out or otherwise circulated without
the publisher's prior consent in any form of binding or cover other than
that in which it is published and without a similar condition, including
this condition, being imposed upon the subsequent purchaser.

FIRST TITAN EDITION: AUGUST 1995

SCHOLASTIC SPECIAL EDITION: AUGUST 2001

ISBN 1-84023-375-3

2 4 6 8 10 9 7 5 3 1

Publisher: MATT GROENING
Managing Editor: JASON GRODE
Art Director - Editor: BILL MORRISON
Book Design: MARILYN FRANDSEN
Legal Guardian: SUSAN GRODE
Contributing Artists:
BILL MORRISON, TIM BAVINGTON, PHIL ORTIZ, LUIS ESCOBAR,
STEPHANIE GLADDEN, STEVE VANCE, CINDY VANCE, NATHAN KANE
Contributing Writers:
BILL MORRISON, ANDREW GOTTLIEB, GARY GLASBERG, STEVE VANCE
Printed in Italy by Valprint

CONTENTS

GREETINGS, HUNGRY COMICS FANS!

Right this way, ladies and gentlemen, and welcome to another tasty all-you-can-eat collection of Simpsonoid comical funnies, written, penciled, inked, and simmered just for you by your favorite demented cartoon chefs at Bongo Comics. We've got a special meaty comic-book stew du jour a-bubblin' away on the stove for you this time, full of rich Barty goodness, thick Homerish chunks, and sinewy Lisa-esque fibers. And by popular request, we've added a scoop or two of spicy Maggie-reenos, along with our usual heaping dollops of authentic homemade Snowball II furballs, and, to stretch the meal even further, a jumbo boxful of Santa's Little Helper helper.

A Milhouse salad, of course, comes with every meal at no extra charge. Krustyburgers and Sideshow Mel fries are also available, but the extra-bitter Sideshow Bob soup is off the menu, at least temporarily.

And be sure to save room for dessert! You haven't lived 'til you've tasted a big old gooey bowl of Flanders-style flan, or munched on Mrs. Krabappel's famous crabapples, or chewed on a platterful of hot Itchy cakes drenched in creamy Scratchy sauce.

And if you clean your plate you get a special surprise! (The surprise being the surprised look on our faces that you actually cleaned your plate!)

So come on in, put up your feet, and start gnawing! We may not be the fanciest greasy-spoon hole-in-the-wall in town, but we stand by our slogan: "It's positively Simpslicious!"

What other book would even think of making that claim?

MATT GROENING
Bongo Comics Group

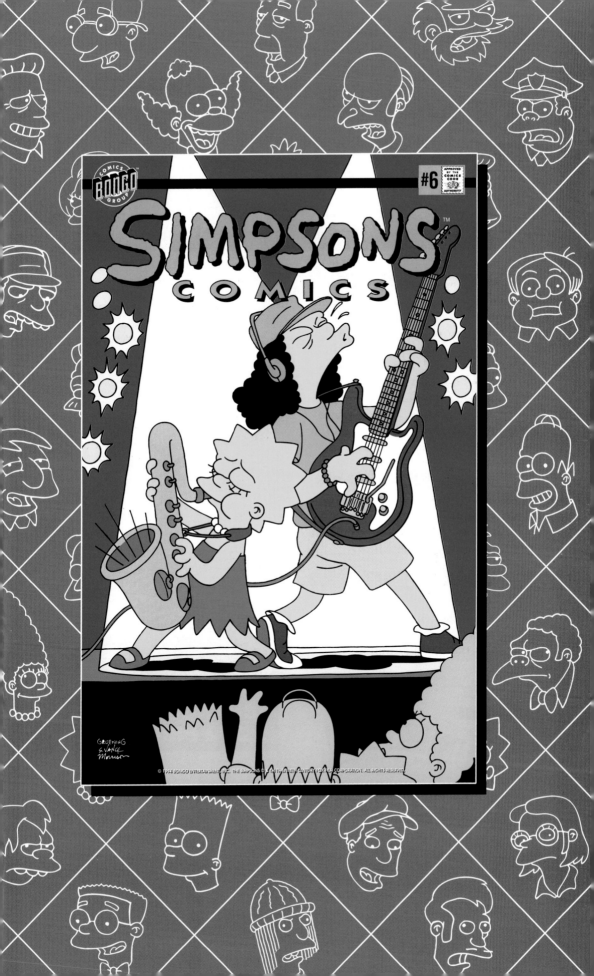

BE-BOP-A-LISA

SPRINGFIELD ELEMENTARY TALENT SHOW

EXIT

JUST AS I SUSPECTED -- MS. KRABAPPEL, TWO-TIMING ME WITH *GROUNDSKEEPER WILLIE*.

:GASP: *PRINCIPAL SKINNER!*

ACH! MIND YOUR OWN BUSINESS, YOU *DOILY-MAKIN' MAMA'S BOY!*

SCRIPT & PENCILS
BILL MORRISON

INKS
TIM BAVINGTON

COLORS
CINDY VANCE

EDITOR
STEVE VANCE

HEAD ROADIE
MATT GROENING

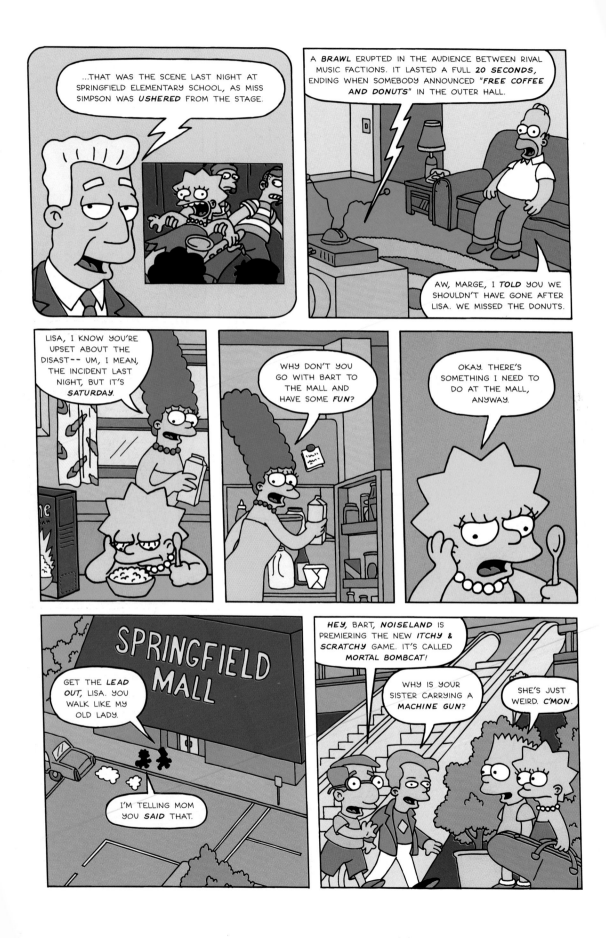

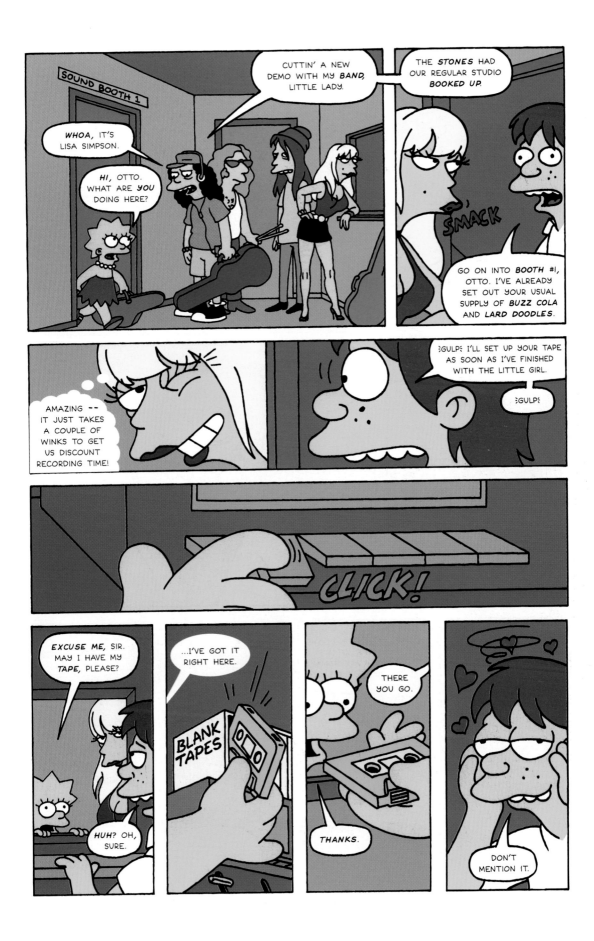

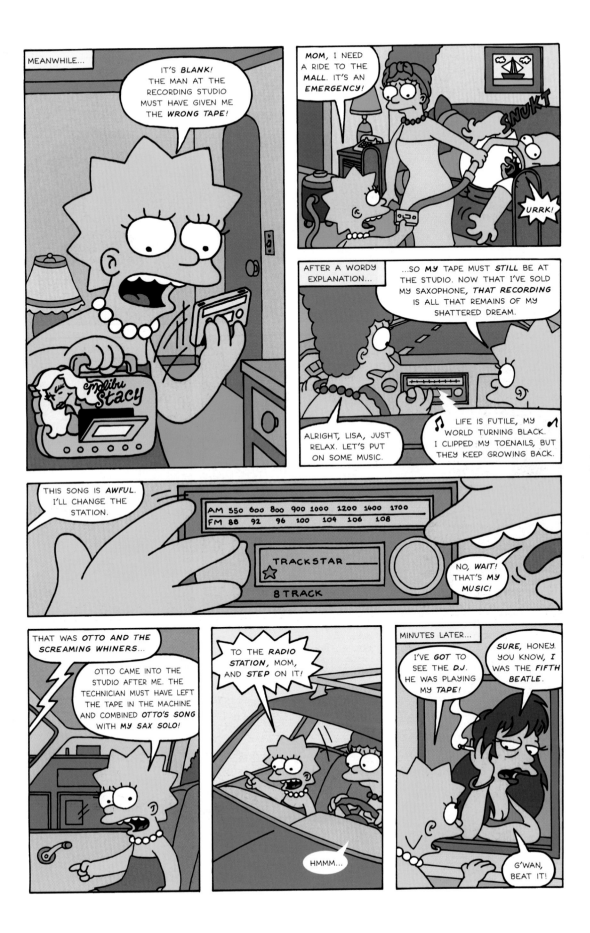

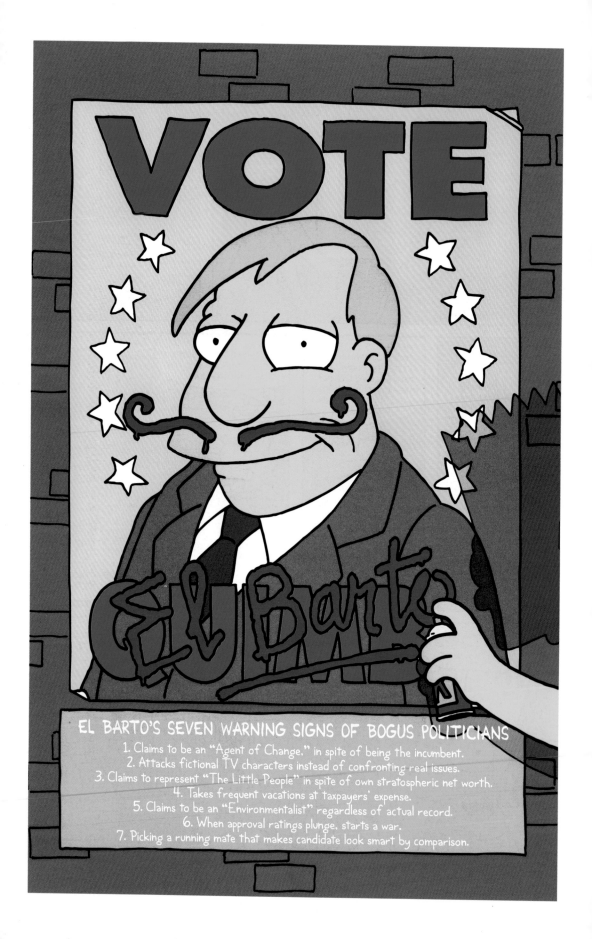

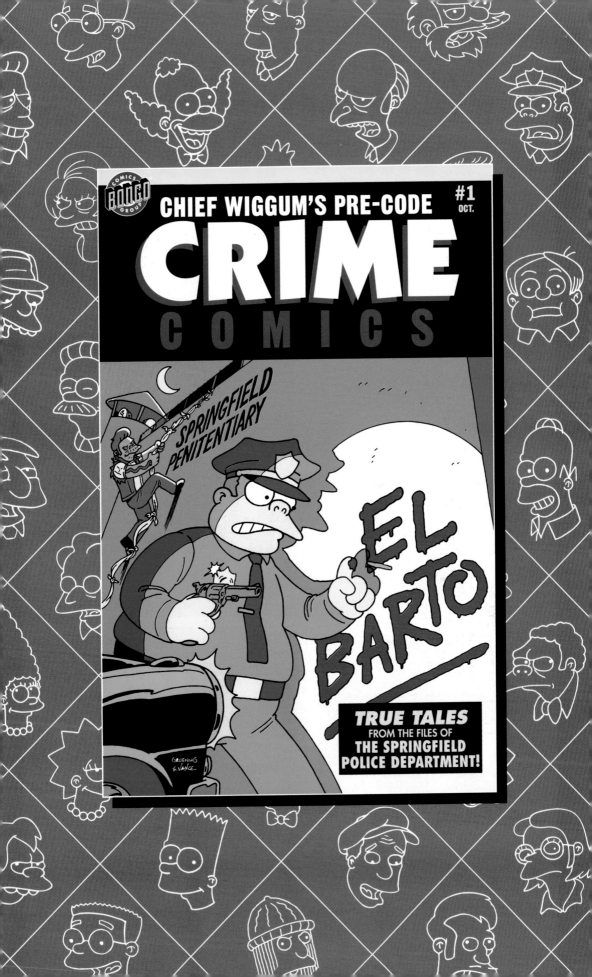

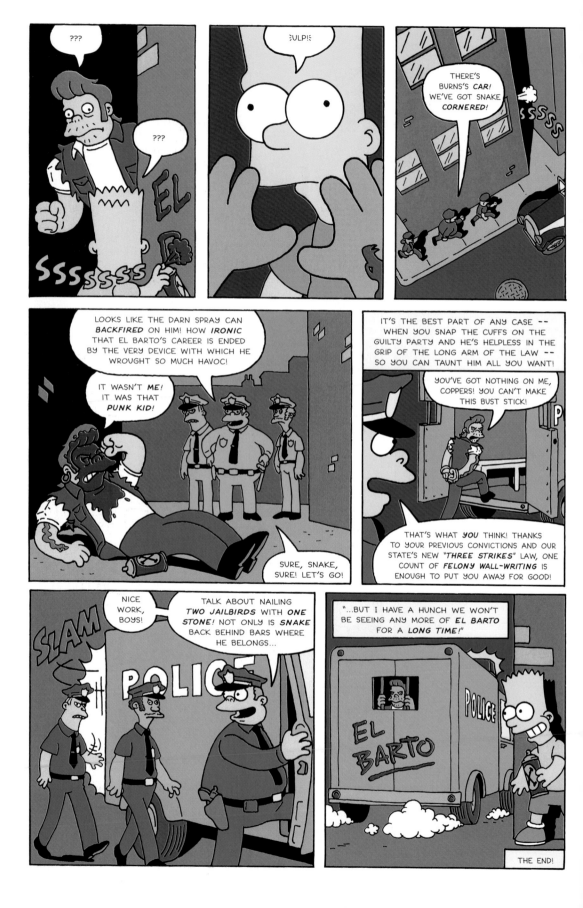

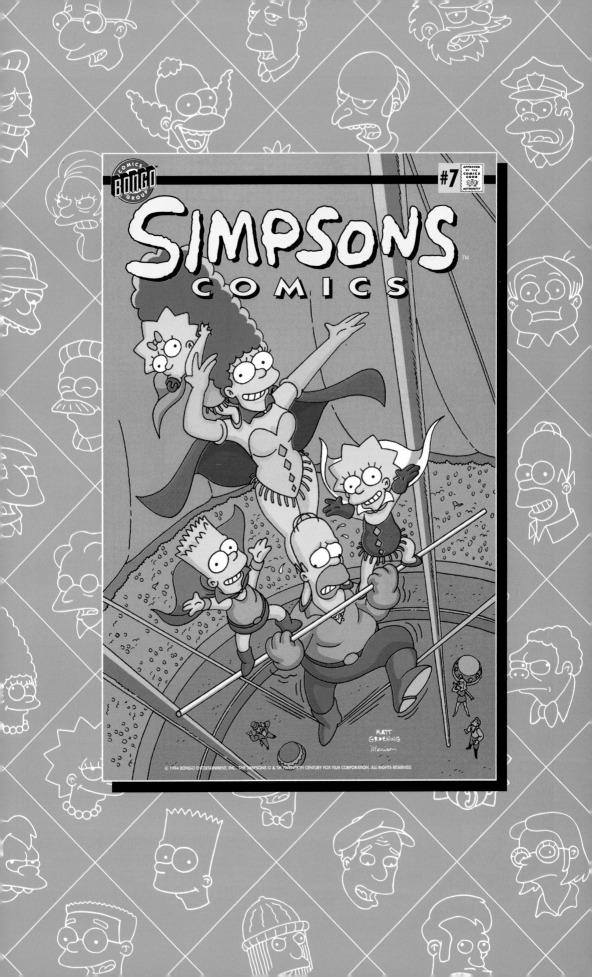

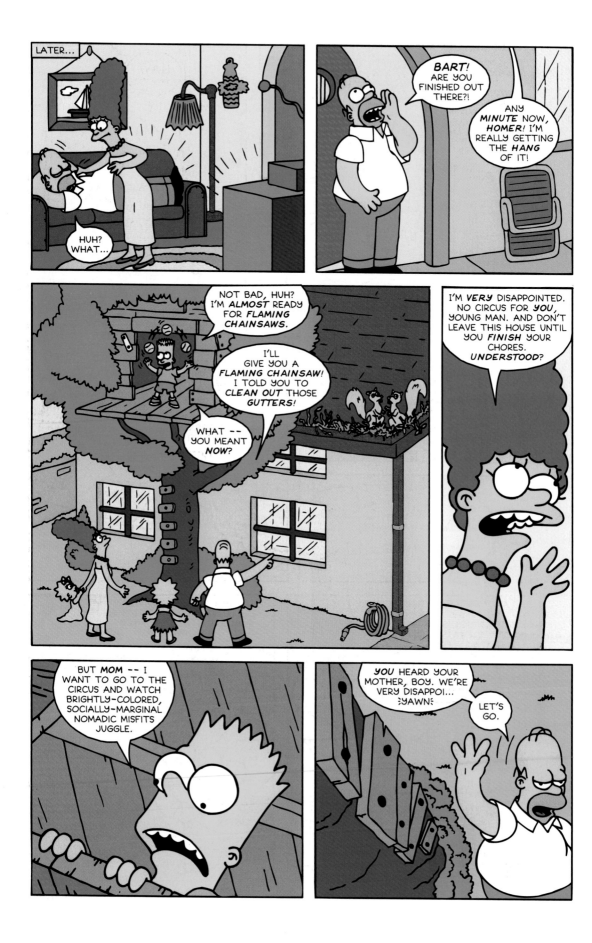

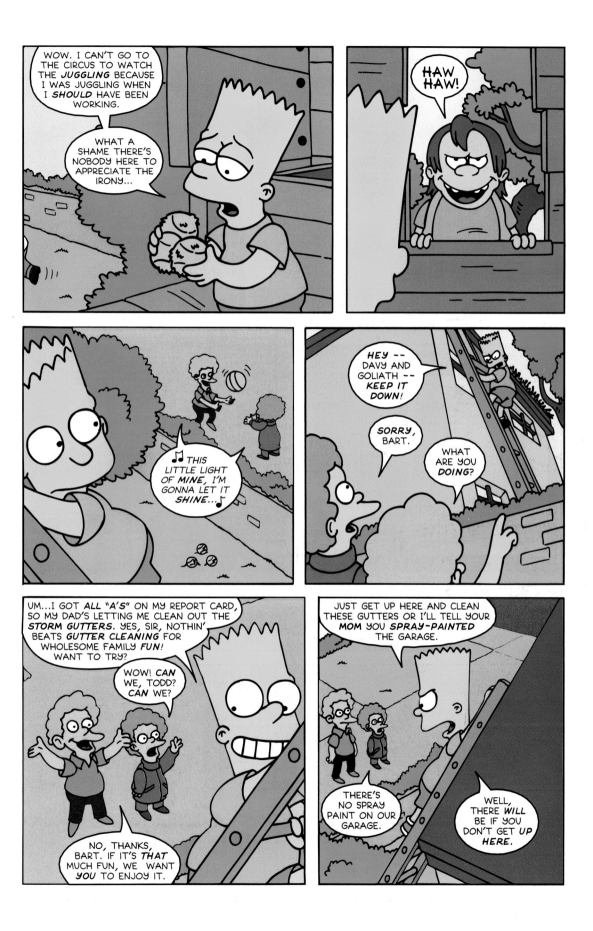

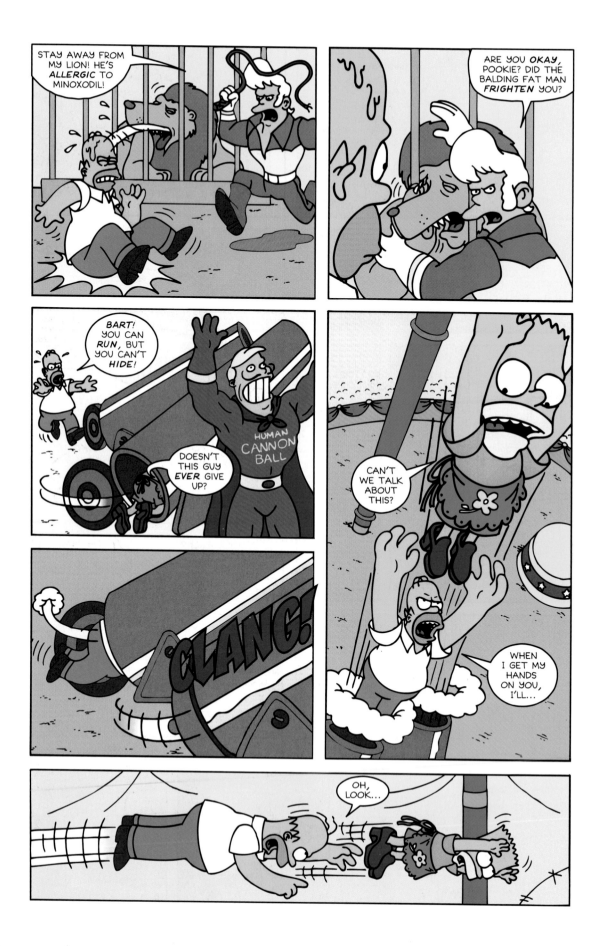

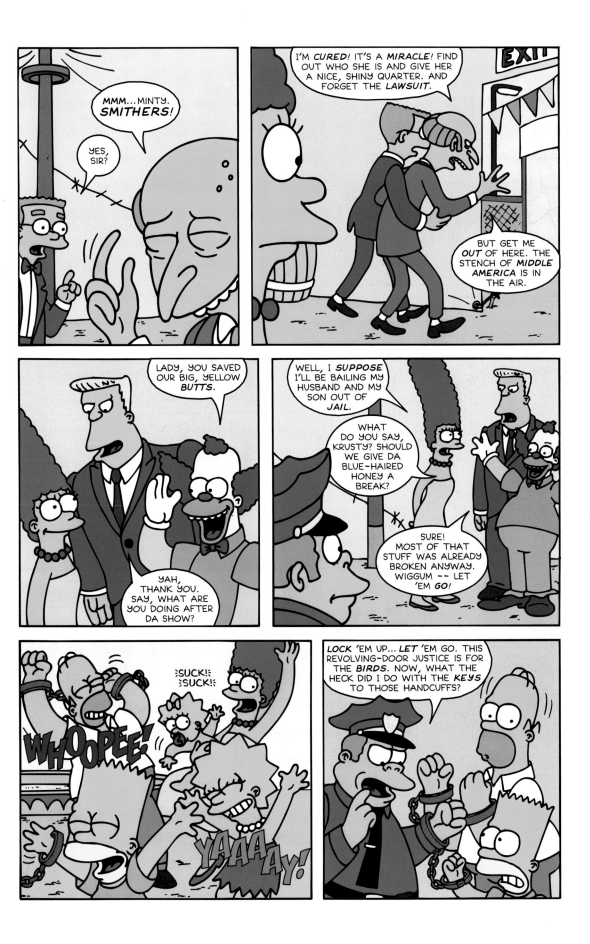

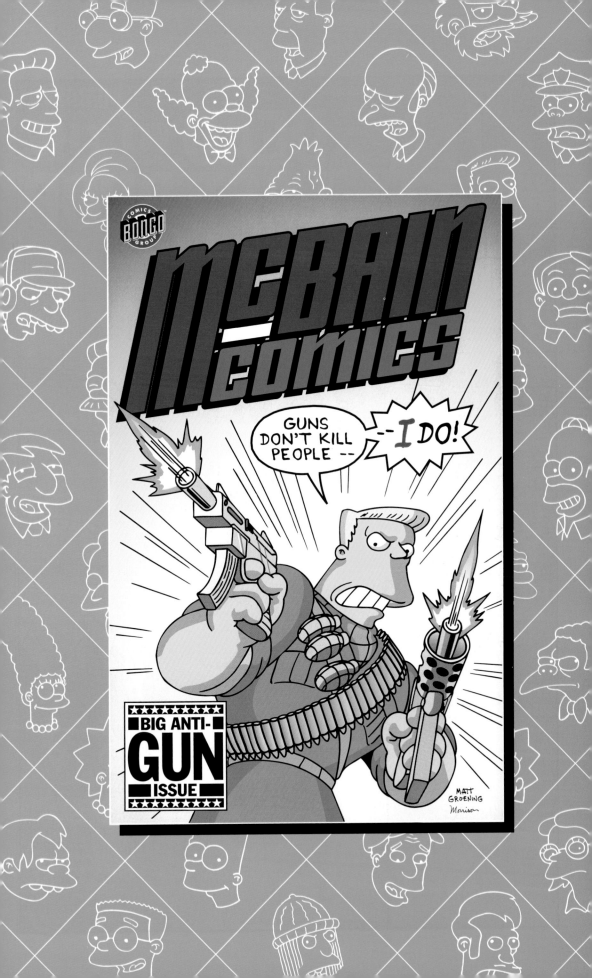

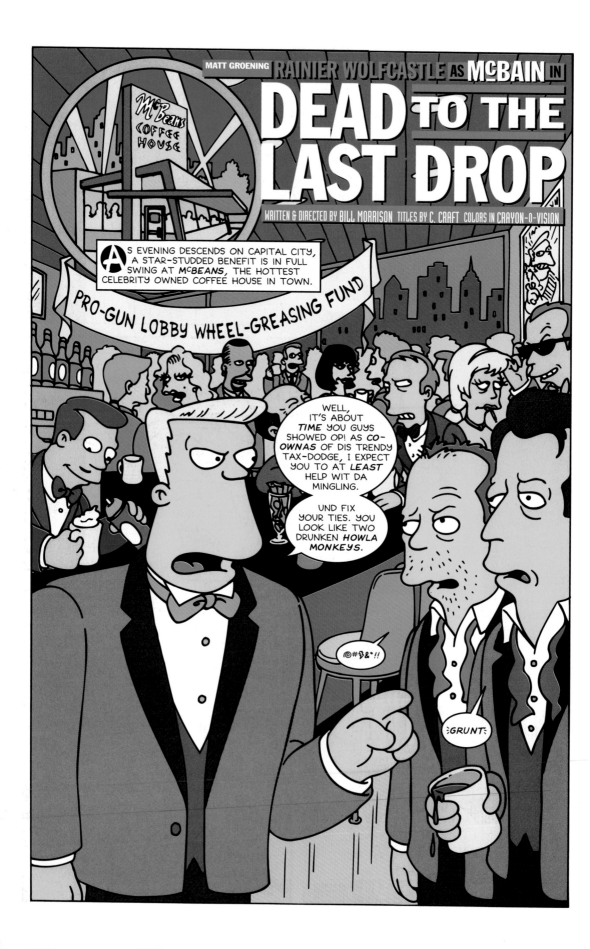

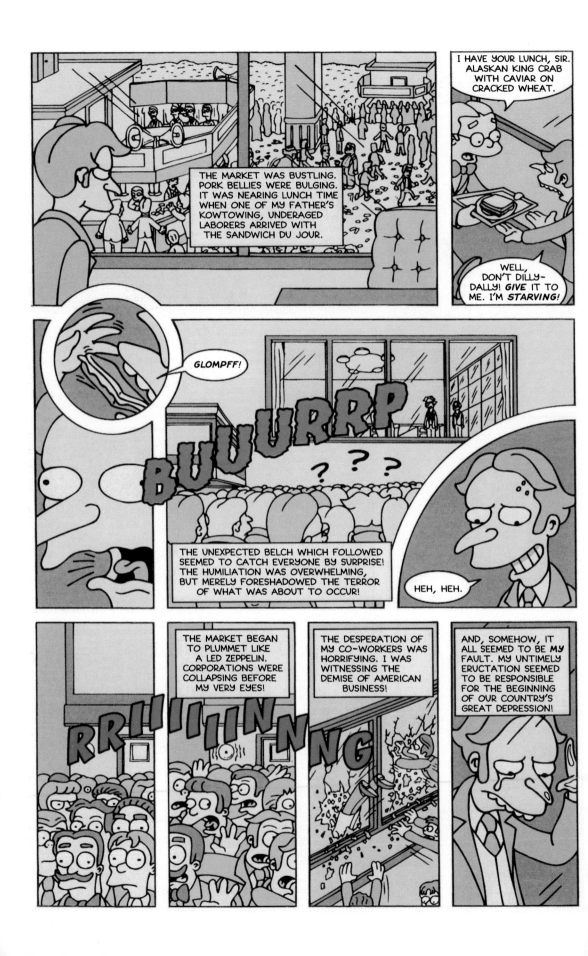

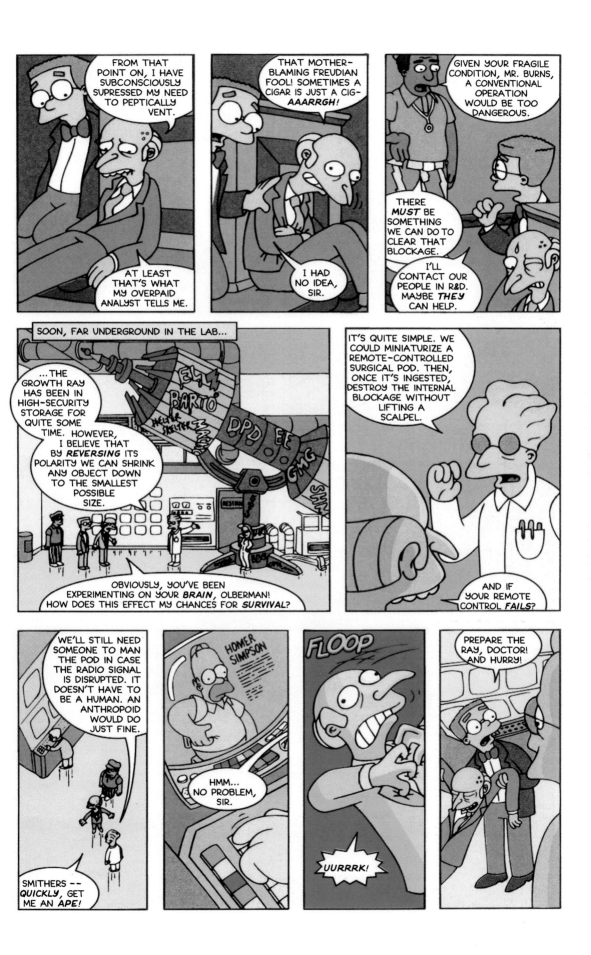

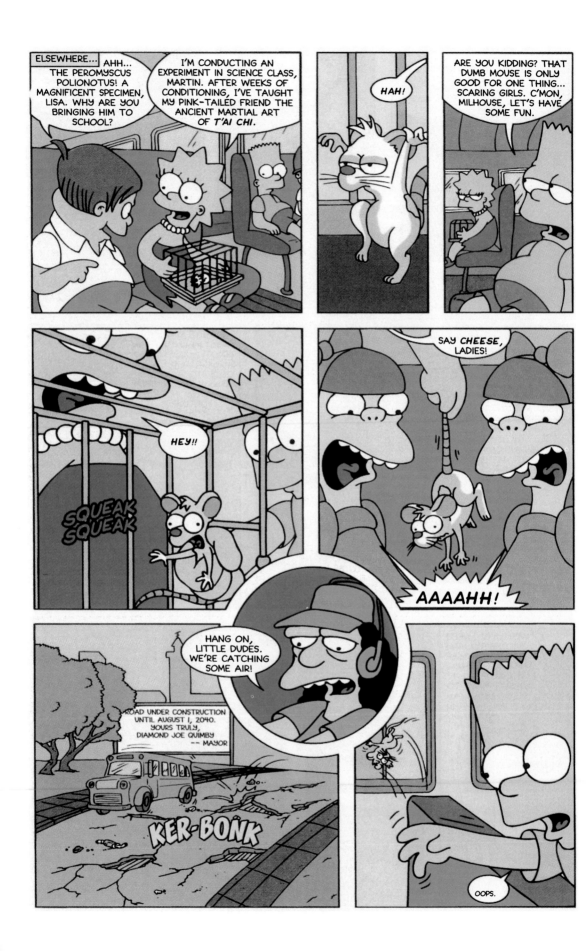

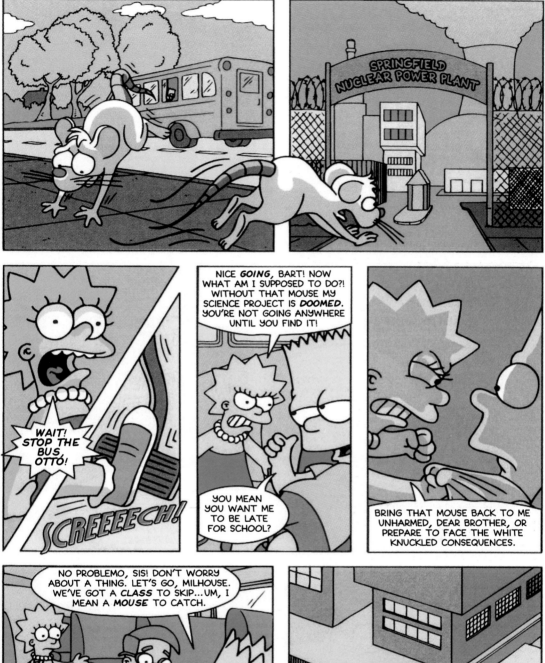

NICE *GOING*, BART! NOW WHAT AM I SUPPOSED TO DO?! WITHOUT THAT MOUSE MY SCIENCE PROJECT IS *DOOMED*. YOU'RE NOT GOING ANYWHERE UNTIL YOU FIND IT!

WAIT! STOP THE BUS, OTTO!

SCREEEECH!

YOU MEAN YOU WANT ME TO BE LATE FOR SCHOOL?

BRING THAT MOUSE BACK TO ME UNHARMED, DEAR BROTHER, OR PREPARE TO FACE THE WHITE KNUCKLED CONSEQUENCES.

NO PROBLEMO, SIS! DON'T WORRY ABOUT A THING. LET'S GO, MILHOUSE. WE'VE GOT A *CLASS* TO SKIP...UM, I MEAN A *MOUSE* TO CATCH.

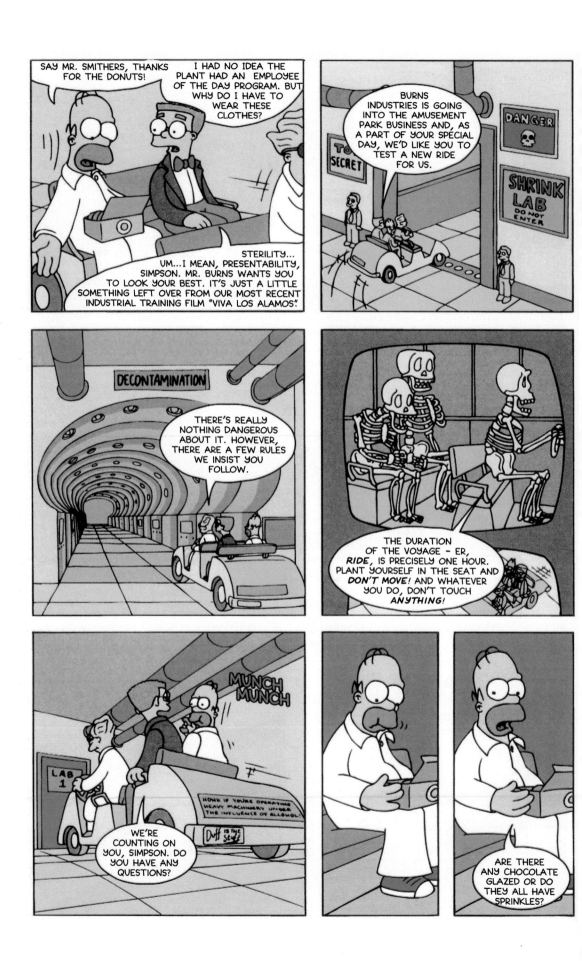

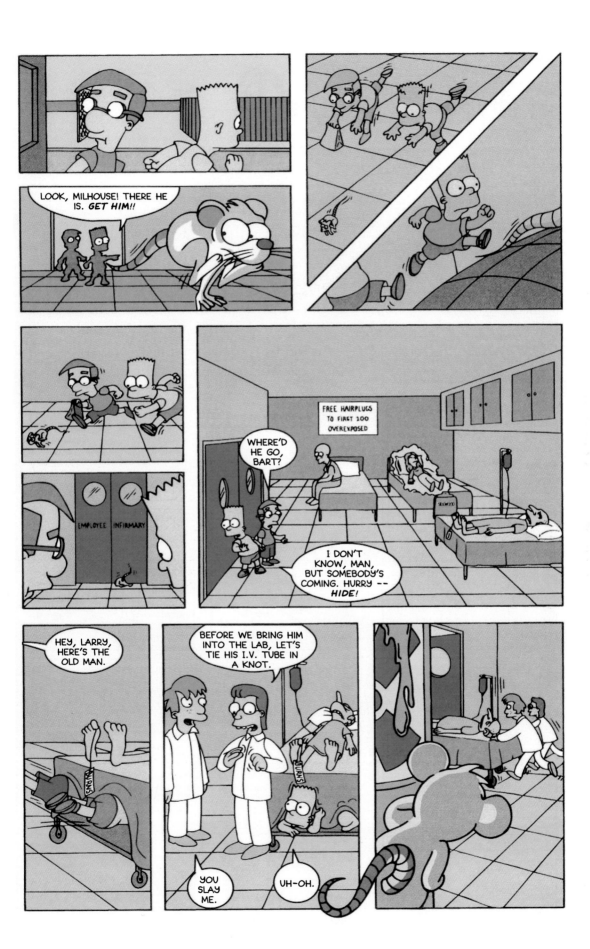

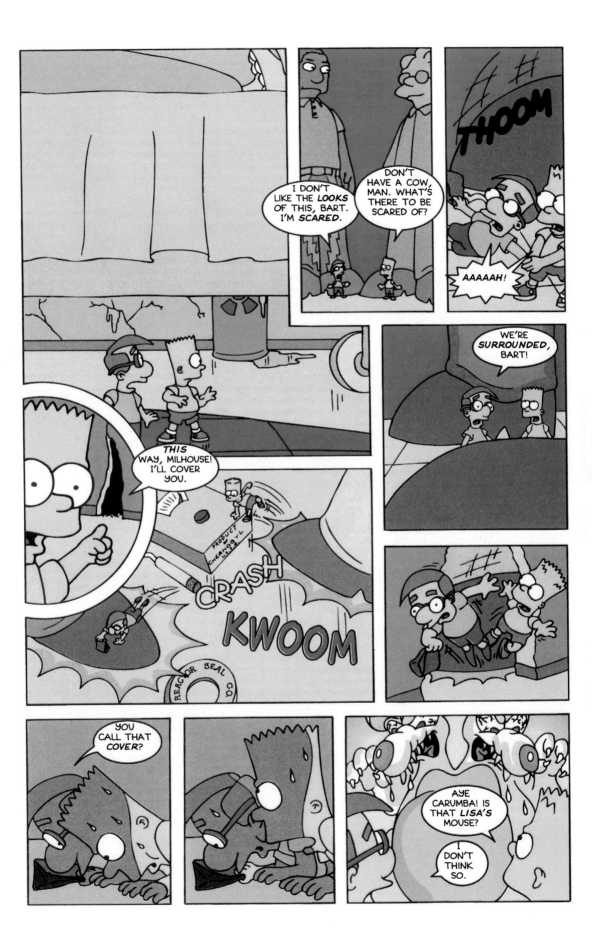

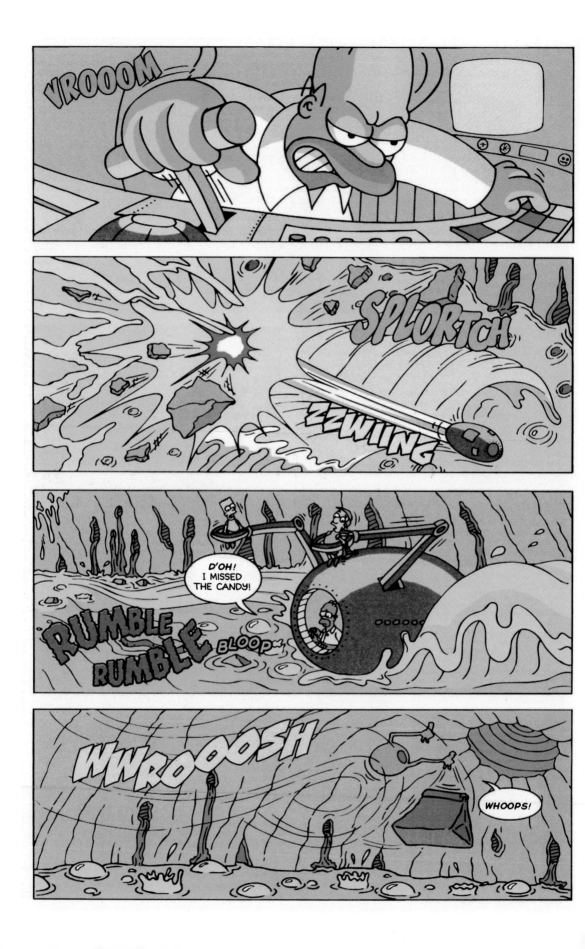

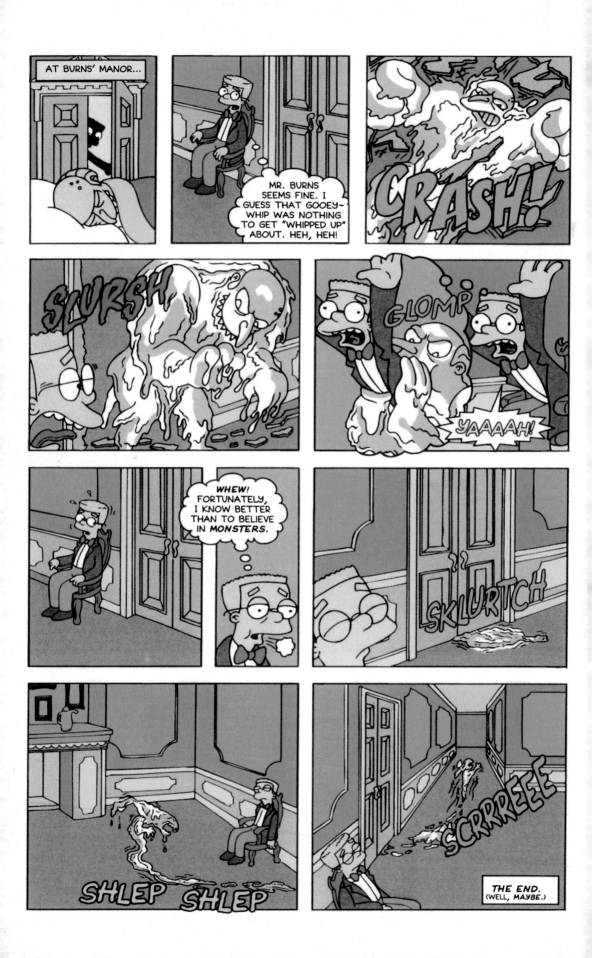

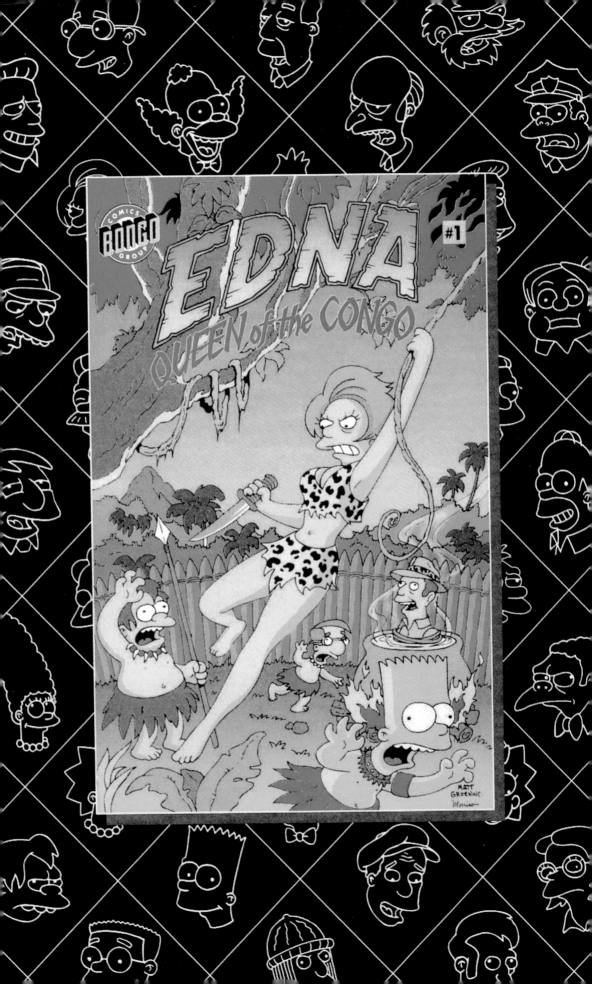

THE END

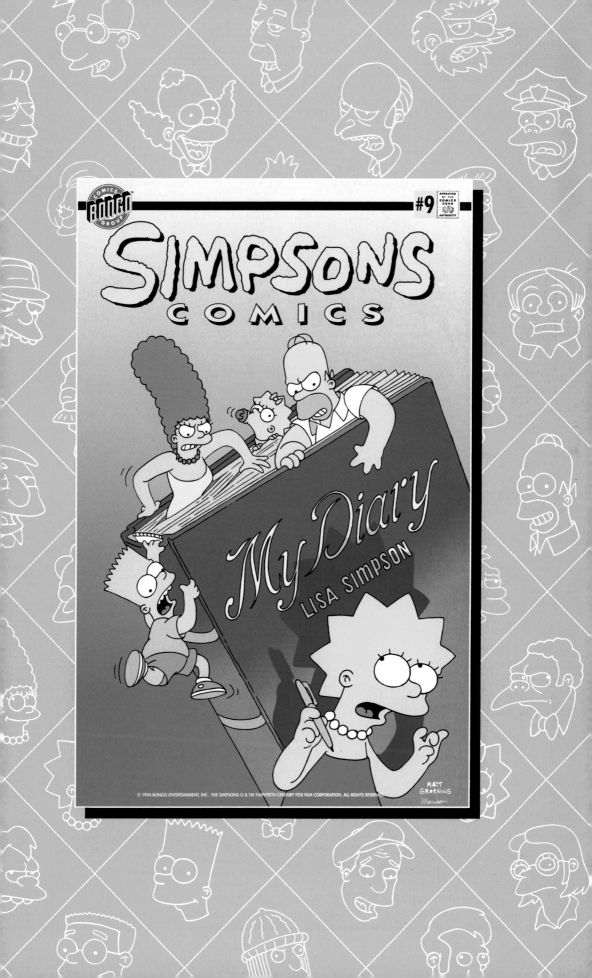

THE PURPLE PROSE OF SPRINGFIELD

ENEMY CAMP DESERTED. DON'T KNOW HOW LONG STORM GUTTER CAN SUPPORT MY WEIGHT...

...WHOA!

ANDREW GOTTLIEB
SCRIPT

LUIS ESCOBAR
PENCILS

TIM BAVINGTON
INKS

STARKINGS/ COMICRAFT
LETTERING

ELECTRIC CRAYON
COLORS

MATT GROENING
STETISTICIAN

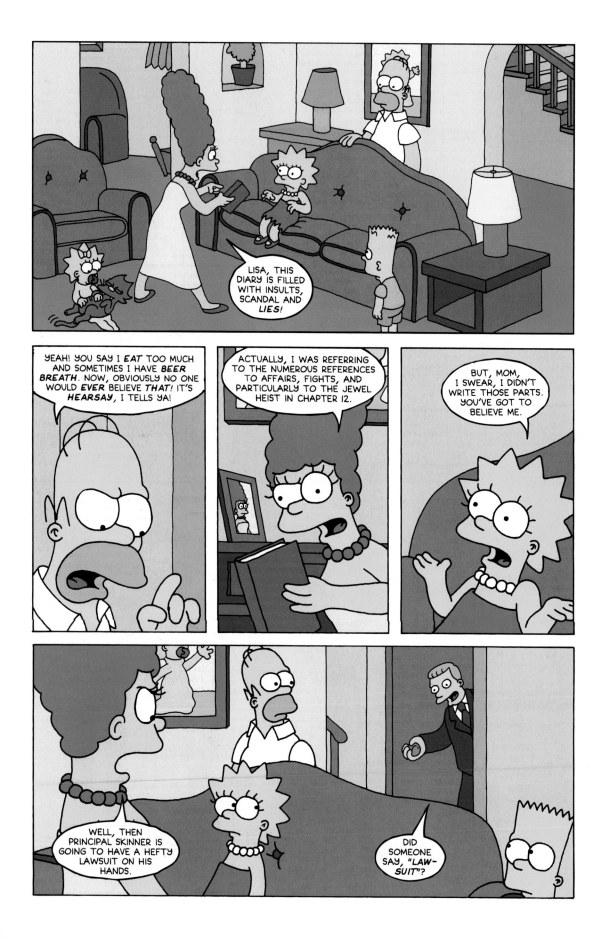

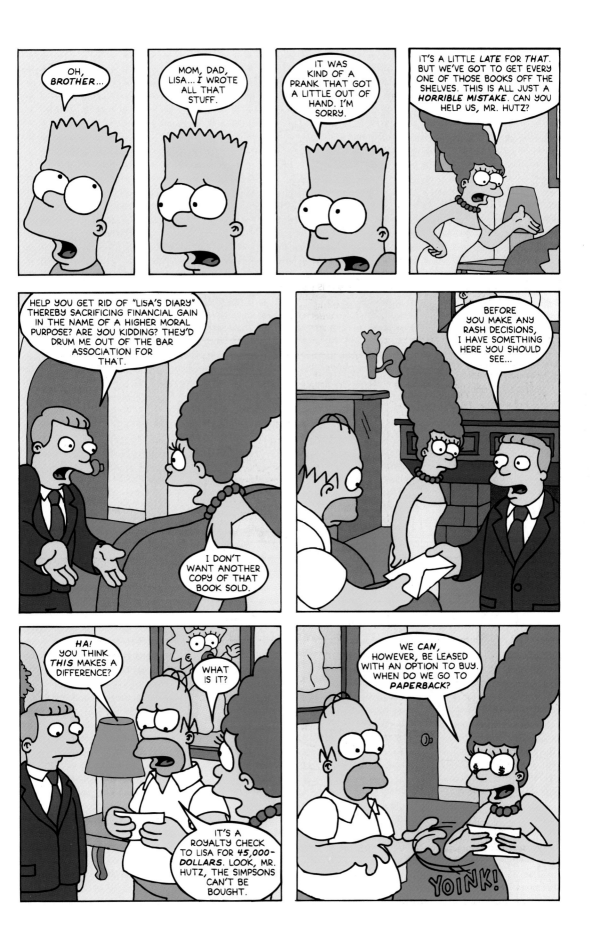

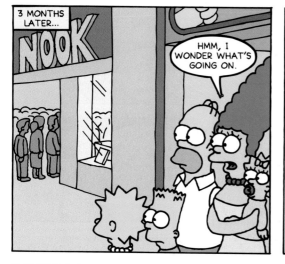

HOMER SIMPSON'S PATHETIC PAL BARNEY IN:

ASLEEP AT THE WELL

MONDAY, 9:02 AM...

MORNIN' MOE!

HEY, BARNEY. WHAT'RE *YOU* DOING HERE SO EARLY?

MOE'S TAVERN

MOE'S

BILL MORRISON STORY	STEPHANIE GLADDEN PENCILS	TIM BAVINGTON INKS	STARKINGS/ COMICRAFT LETTERING	ELECTRIC CRAYON COLORS	MATT GROENING BRAUMEISTER

MY NEW ROOMMATE THREW A *WILD PARTY* AT OUR APARTMENT LAST NIGHT. IT WAS SO *NOISY* THERE, I COULDN'T FALL ASLEEP...

...SO I DECIDED TO COME *HERE*.

OKAY, BUT REMEMBER, THIS AIN'T NO *FLOPHOUSE!*

10:15 AM...

ZZZZZ...

MORNING, MOE. GIMME A GLASS OF MILK.

COMIN' UP.

GULP!

SPEW!

WHAT'RE YOU TRYIN' TO DO, KILL ME? THAT WAS *REAL MILK!*

SMACK

OH, RIGHT! THE *CODE!*

SORRY CHIEF. I'LL REMEMBER NEXT TIME.

WIGGUM'S CODE

MILK = WHITE RUSSIAN

CHERRY SODA = SLOE GIN FIZZ

BUZZ COLA = HARVEY WALLBANGER

BLACK COFFEE = STRAIGHT KAHLUA

ROOT BEER = ANY KIND OF BEER EXCEPT ROOT BEER

11:35 AM...

ZZZZZ...

C'MON LARRY, HURRY UP WITH THAT *HOT WATER!*

SAM, GET ME SOME CLEAN *BAR RAGS!*

UH, YOU MIGHT WANNA START PUSHIN' NOW, MA'AM.

YOU HEARD THE MAN! C'MON, *PUSH!* MY LUNCH-TIME RUSH IS GONNA START ANY MINUTE!!

NICE *GOIN'*, MISTER!

SMACK

WAAAAH!

THANK YOU. THANK YOU VERY MUCH!

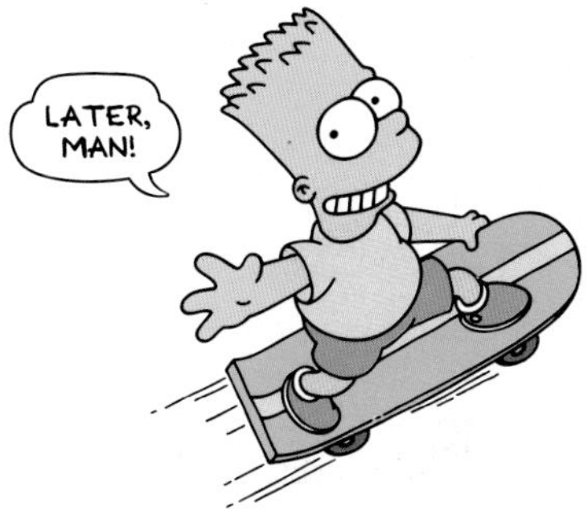
LATER, MAN!